Bernie the Christmas Spirit

Names: Watermeyer, Sean, Author and Williams, Vanessa, Illustrator

Title: Bernie the Christmas Spirit/ by Sean Watermeyer

Description: Cardiff: SABGE Publishing [2020]

ISBN: 9781838069209

Subjects: Christmas, Homelessness, Family, Christmas Spirit

Manufactured in the UK

Written by Sean Watermeyer and Illustrated by Vanessa Williams

Foreword from Centrepoint

All royalties from this book will go to Centrepoint Homelessness Charity

In 2019, 110,000 young people aged 16-25 contacted their local authority to ask for help with homelessness. Centrepoint is the UK's leading charity offering a holistic programme of support for these vulnerable young people. Our ultimate aim is for young people to leave our accommodation services into a home of their own, with the life skills, good mental and physical health and employment prospects that mean they can leave homelessness behind for good. Simply buying this book is helping us achieve this goal, so thank you.

—————— IN AID OF ——————

Written by Sean Watermeyer

Illustrated by Vanessa Williams

When Christmas carols echo, and snow is on the ground.
When our parks are full of snowmen and decorations are all around.

Bernie appears, a wee friendly spirit, of love and wholesome cheer.
He visits us at Christmas time, every single year.

Bernie enters into our hearts and fills us all with
Christmas glee
He fills us all with Christmas joy and makes our troubles
flee.

Bernie tickles us to laughter, encourages us to care
All our hurts and sadness, he helps us all to bear.

Now one snowy Christmas Eve, when Bernie was floating about
He saw a young man, his clothes in rags, the light in his eyes gone out.

His Hair was dirty and knotted, he sat upon a rag
His worldly possessions by his side in a plastic carrier bag.

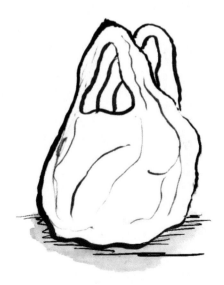

The people, they all walked on by,
as the young man sat and shivered. So
Bernie flew around them, his Christmas
spirit delivered.

But despite the goodness of his spirit, their hearts remained so cold.
Despite what Christ the Lord had said, despite what they had been told.

So then Bernie became all sad, for goodness had started
to dwindle
Love was needed, from somewhere, to help the little
spirit rekindle.

As the people continued to ignore that lad, Bernie
started to disappear
And as the little spirit faded so too did love and
Christmas cheer.

And just when he thought that all was lost, with her
Mum and Dad she came
Laughing and dancing down the street, and Mary was
her name.

Bernie could see she was full of love, untainted by the
world's cruel way
She stopped and looked, and looked again on that
snowy Christmas Eve day.

Mary went right up to that young man and looked into
his sad and lonely eyes
And Bernie saw the lad look up, on his face a look of
surprise.

Then Mary took out her Christmas purse and gave him
all she had
"Merry Christmas" she whispered softly, and Bernie
with joy went mad.

The little spirit re-energised and whizzed happily around the place. Soon every man, woman and child, had a smile upon their face.

Mary's example showed
them all, the path to Christmas love and joy.
She showed them that giving to those in need,
was better than any toy.

The lad was shown love, given food and shelter,
that cold Christmas Eve night

And the world was just a little bit better, for what had
been done was right.

There is a little spirit called Bernie in each of us who
care

That little spirit is God's love, and He is everywhere!

Printed in Poland
by Amazon Fulfillment
Poland Sp. z o.o., Wrocław

64026060R00016